P9-CCO-832

FOR AUDIO
THE GREATEST PERSON
I KNOW

BY DALLAS CLAYTON

THERE ARE PLACES IN THE WORLD
WHERE PEOPLE DO NOT DREAM...

OF ROCKET-POWERED UNICORNS™

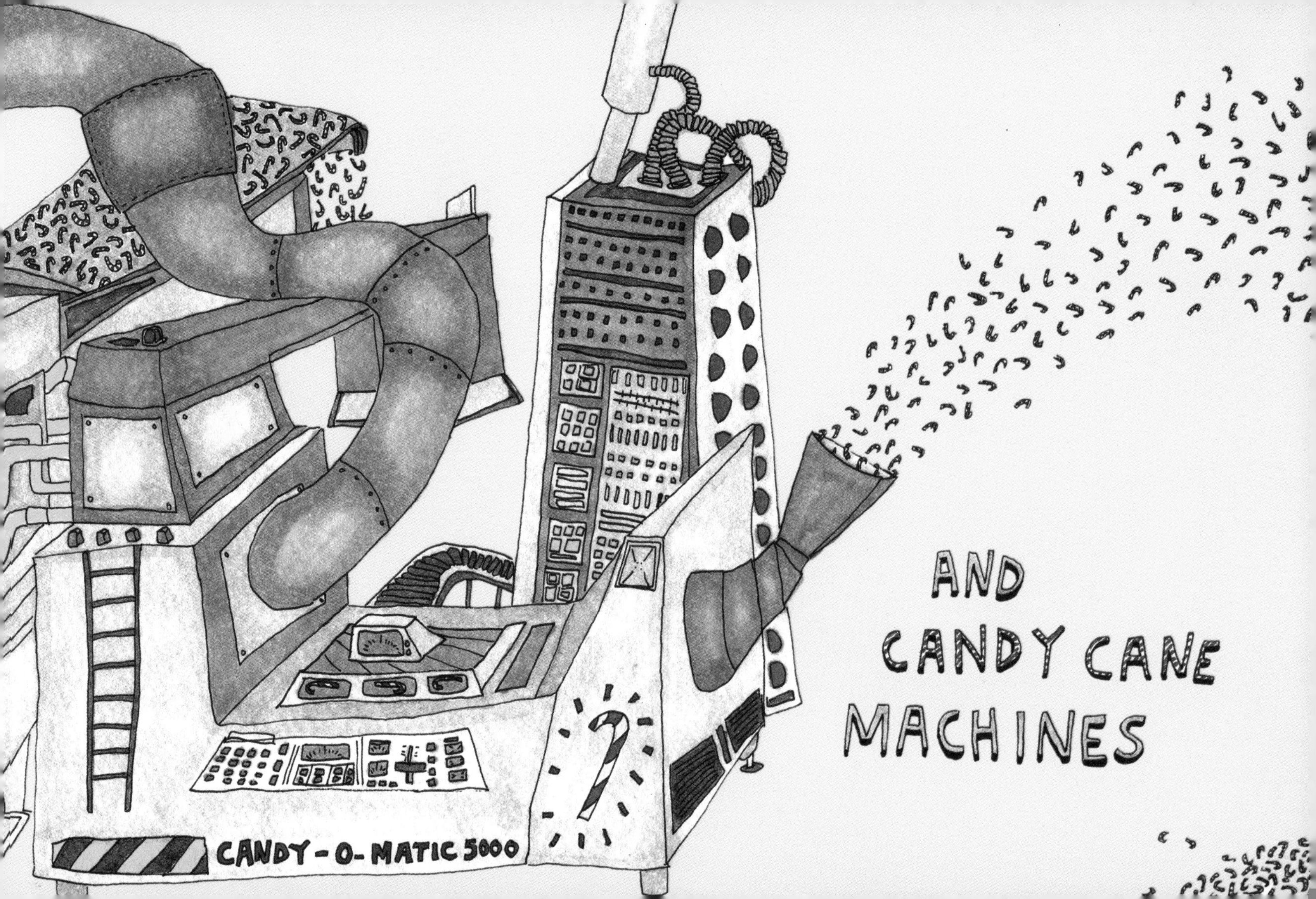

AND CANDY CANE MACHINES

OF MAGIC WATERMELON
BOATS

AND MUSICAL
BABOONS

OR TEENY TINY
TRUMPET PLAYERS

TRAINING PET RACCOONS

YES THERE ARE PLACES IN THE WORLD WHERE PEOPLE DREAM UP DREAMS

SO SIMPLY UN-FANTASTICAL
AND PRACTICAL
THEY SEEM...

TO LOSE ALL POSSIBILITY OF THINKING SUPER THINGS

BUS STOP

OF DANCING WILD ANIMALS

WITH DIAMOND-COATED WINGS

INSTEAD THEY DREAM OF
FURNITURE

OF BUYING A NEW HAT

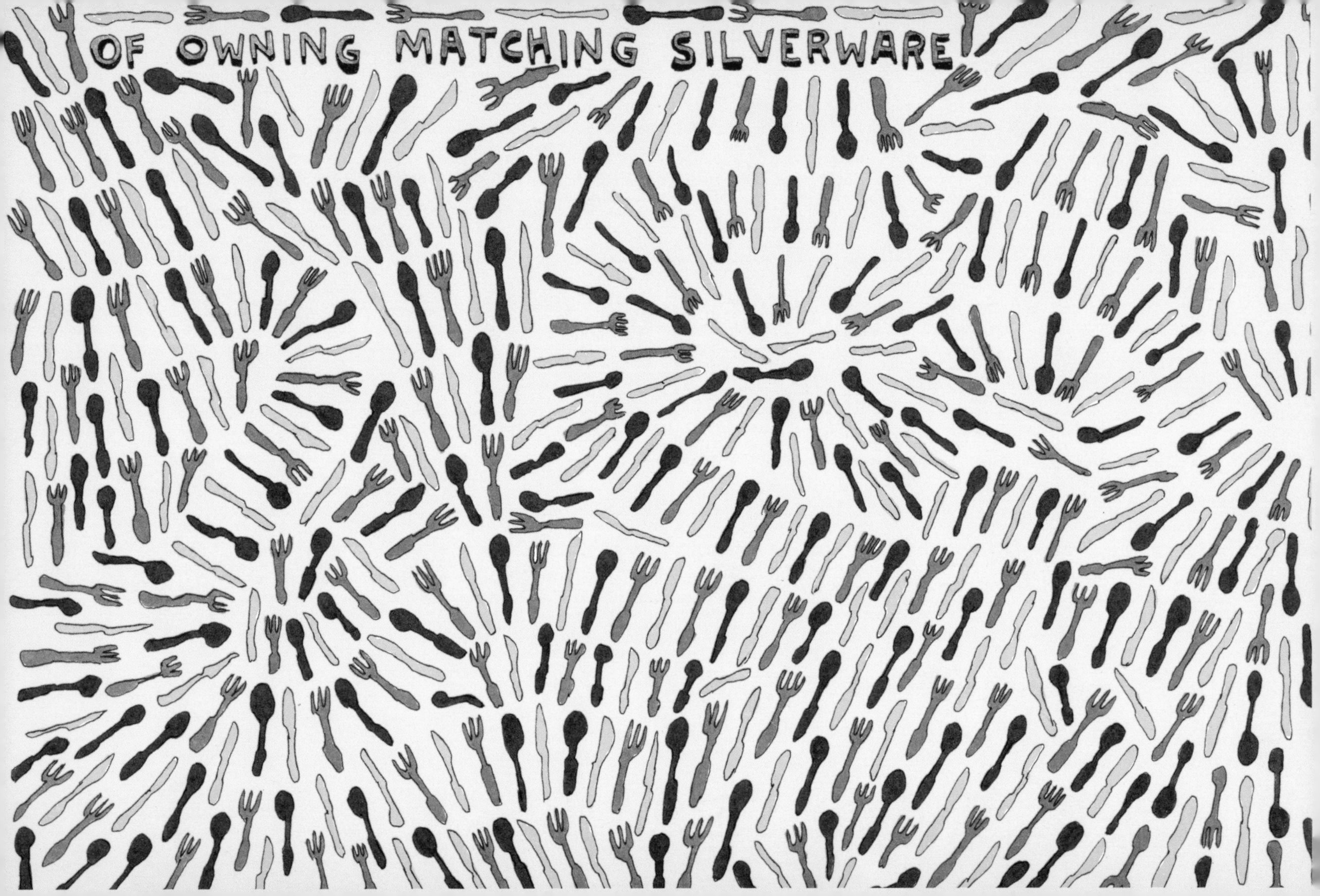
OF OWNING MATCHING SILVERWARE

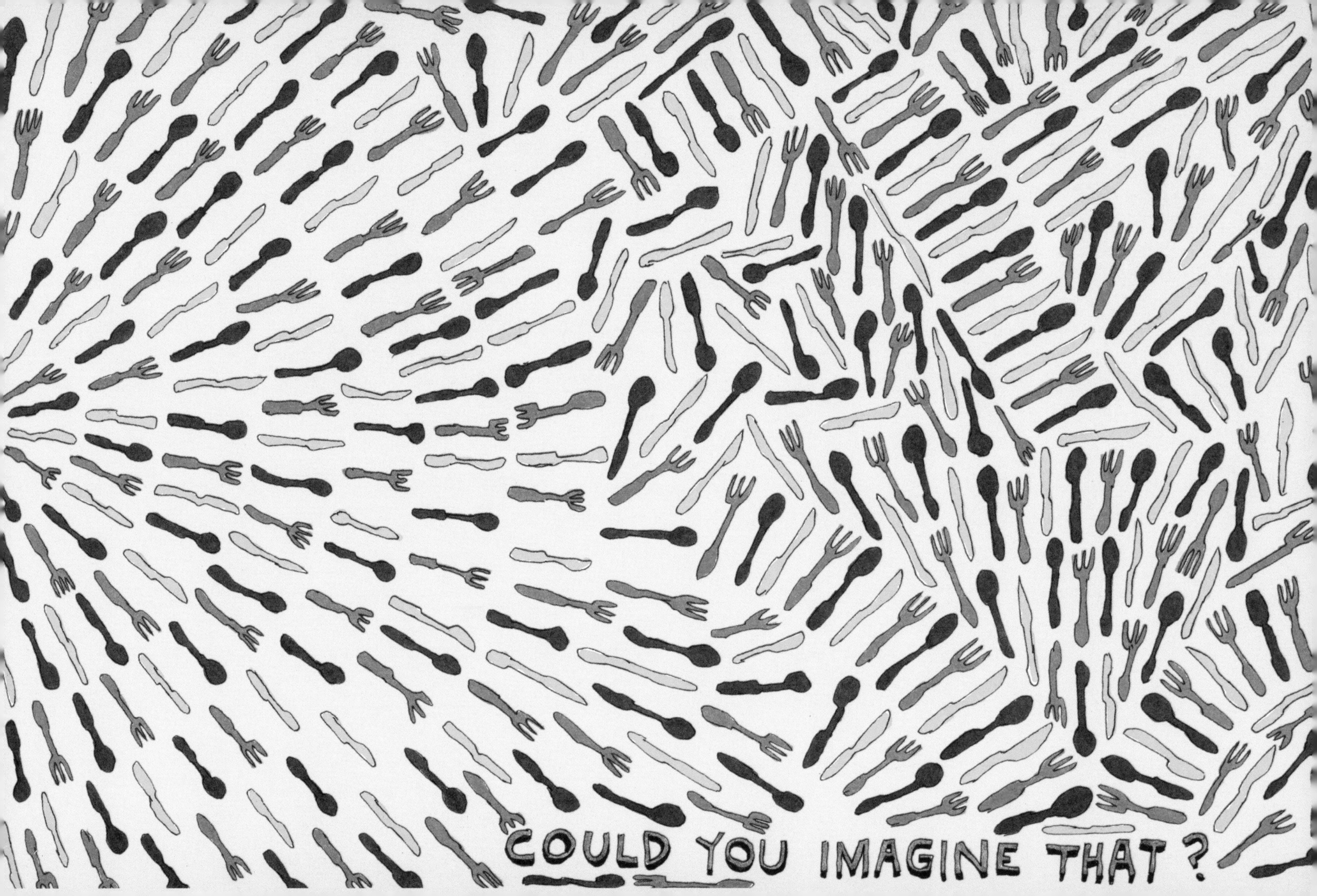
COULD YOU IMAGINE THAT?

INSTEAD THEY LAY AWAKE AT NIGHT
WISHING FOR A CAR

UNLEADED
NOT ONE THAT RUNS ON
JELLYBEANS ...
BUT ONE THAT'S REG-U-LAR

THEY DREAM OF
BREAKFAST SANDWICHES
THEY DREAM

OF
TELEPHONES
SOMETIMES THEY EVEN DREAM
OF DREAMS THAT ARE'NT
EVEN THEIR OWN

YES THERE ARE PLACES IN THE WORLD
WHERE DREAMS ARE ALMOST DEAD

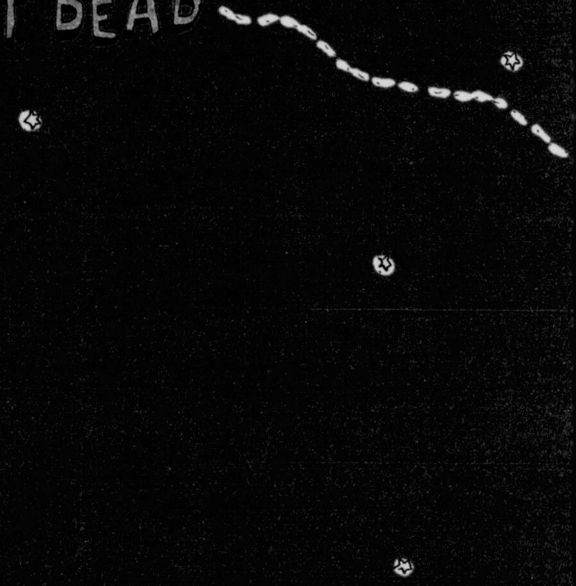

SO PLEASE MY CHILD DO
KEEP IN MIND
BEFORE YOU GO TO BED . . .

TO DREAM A DREAM AS BIG
AS BIG COULD EVER DREAM TO BE

THEN DREAM A DREAM TEN TIMES AS BIG

AS THAT
ONE
DREAM
YOU
SEE

THEN ONCE YOU'VE GOT THAT DREAM
IN MIND PLEASE DREAM
A MILLION MORE

AND NOT A MILLION
QUIET DREAMS
A MILLION DREAMS THAT
ROAR

A MILLION DREAMS
SO LOUD THEY SCREAM

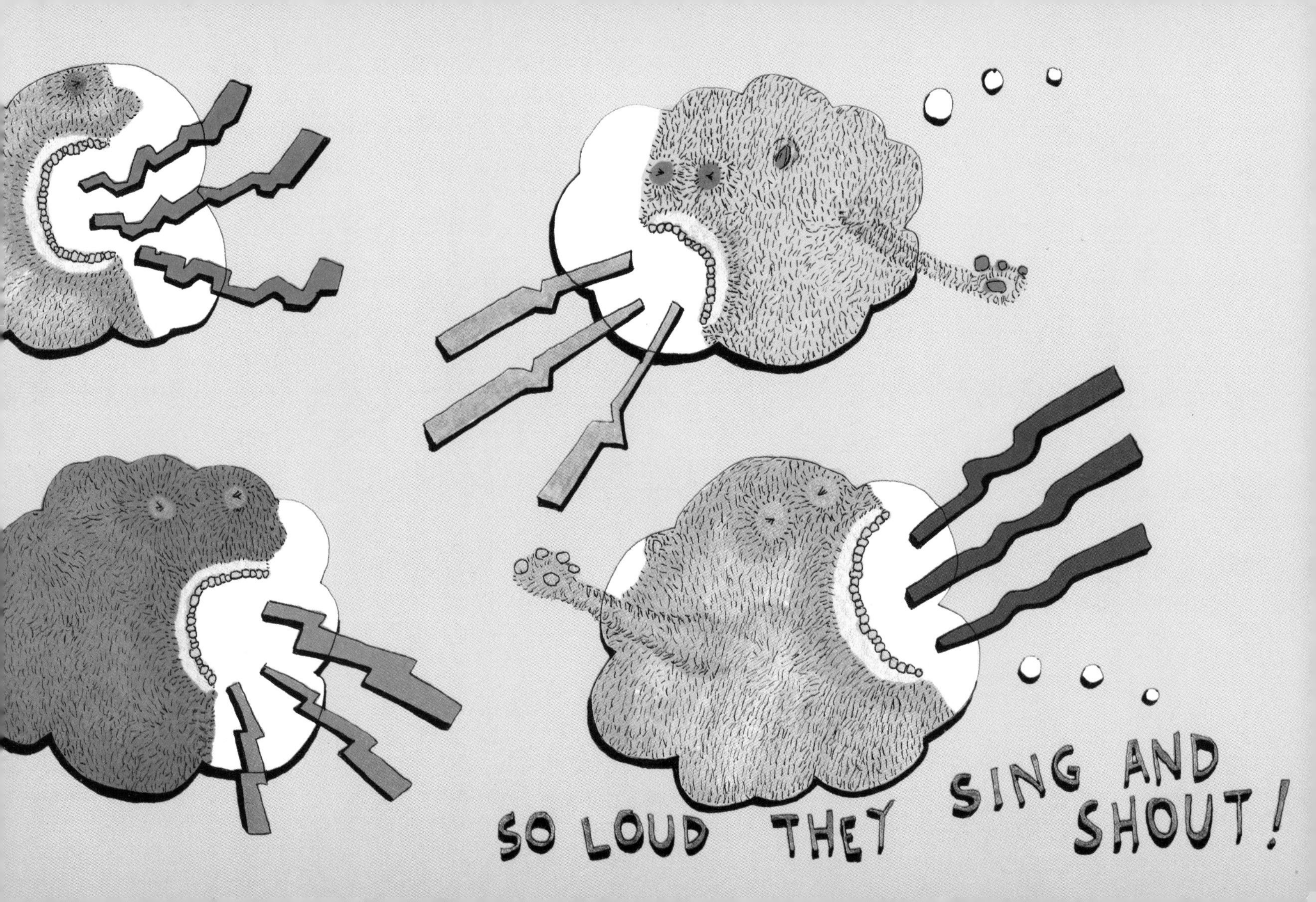
SO LOUD THEY SING AND SHOUT!

SO
SUPER HUGE
THEY SAY "HEY WORLD!
GUESS WHAT I'M
DREAMIN'
BOUT"

"I'M DREAMING ABOUT EVERYTHING THAT NO ONE THOUGHT TO WONDER

DREAMS SO BIG THAT
THEY'VE GOT DREAMS AND
THEY'VE GOT DREAMS
UP UNDER!"

PLEASE DREAM FOR THOSE WHO'VE GIVEN UP

DON'T TRY
FOR THOSE WHO'VE NEVER TRIED

PLEASE USE YOUR
DREAMS TO MAKE NEW
DREAMS

WHATEVER DREAMS
YOU WANT
happy birthday

WHOSE DREAMS CAN CHANGE THE WAY THINGS ARE

AND THE WAY
THAT THINGS ARE NOT

AND IF THEY SAY THAT ALL YOUR DREAMS ARE TOO BIG TO COME TRUE

YOU TELL THEM
THAT I
TOLD
YOU...

"THAT'S WHAT DREAMS ARE MEANT TO DO!"

THEY'RE MEANT TO MAKE YOU SEEM
AS IF YOU DON'T KNOW UP FROM DOWN

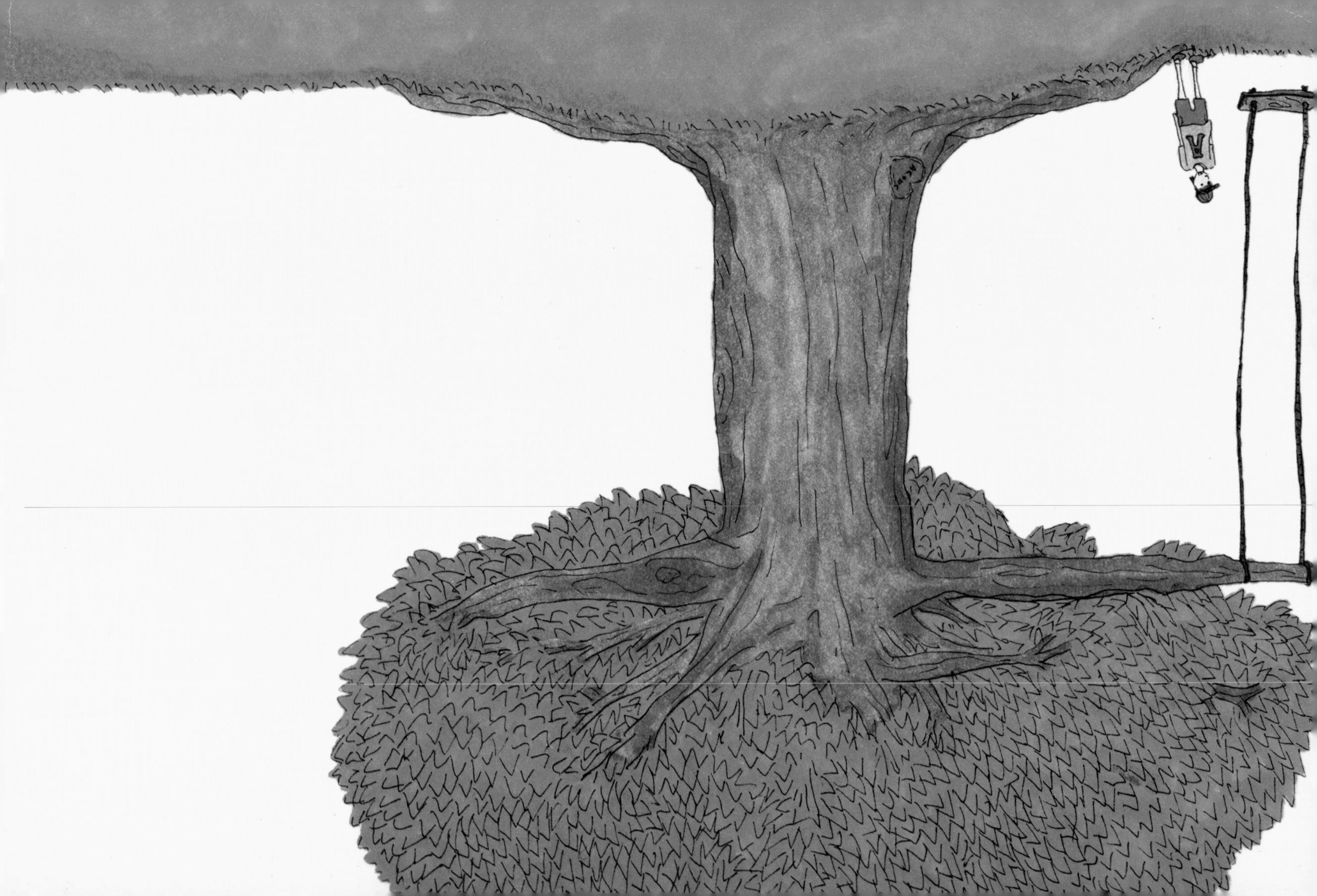

BECAUSE DREAMS ARE DREAMS
AND THAT'S WHY DREAMS ARE
WORTH HAVING AROUND!

SO WHEN YOU THINK YOUR DREAMING'S DONE

JUST REMEMBER
WHAT I SAID

"CLOSE YOUR EYES MY CHILD
AND DREAM
THAT PERFECT DREAM
INSIDE YOUR HEAD"

DALLAS CLAYTON
IS A WRITER, ILLUSTRATOR,
AND CREATOR OF ALL THINGS
GOOD.

THE END